D1482150

Roads to Reasoning

Developing Thinking Skills Through Problem Solving

Stephen Krulik and

Jesse A. Rudnick

Wright Group
McGraw-Hill

Acknowledgments

Project Editors
Mary Euretig, Darlene York

Authors
Stephen Krulik, Jesse A. Rudnick

Design Director
Karen Stack

Cover Design and Illustration
Aki Nurosi

Design
Gerta Sorensen

Illustration
Susan Aiello Studio

Composition
Graphic Advantage, Ltd.

ISBN 0-7622-1350-7
Customer Service 800-624-0822 or 708-385-0110
www.creativepublications.com

1 2 3 4 5 6 7 8 VHG 06 05 04 03 02 01

Contents

Introduction

Rationale

MOST MATHEMATICS EDUCATORS AGREE that the development of reasoning power is a primary objective of elementary mathematics. In fact, problem solving, which is the basis for developing reasoning power, has been at the forefront of the mathematics curriculum for many years. The National Council of Teachers of Mathematics' *Principles and Standards,* released in 2000, continues to emphasize both of these areas. Within the thinking and reasoning domain, the area that requires the greatest attention is the development of higher order thinking skills, specifically critical and creative thinking.

Critical thinking is the ability to analyze a situation and draw appropriate and correct conclusions from the given data. It includes determining inconsistent data, missing data, and extraneous information.

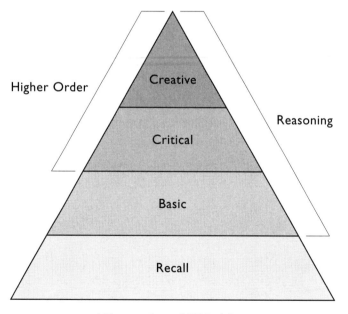

Hierarchy of Thinking

Creative thinking is the ability to originate a solution to a problem situation. In addition, it is the ability to generate, synthesize, and apply original ideas to produce a complex product.

Reasoning is the ultimate goal of the books in this series. Problem solving is the road that will lead to an increased ability to reason. The problems in this book are vehicles that carry the students along the road, and the teacher is the driver who guides the students.

Most mathematics textbook series include some degree of problem solving. This series provides additional practice using a variety of approaches that will further develop reasoning power. As students experience a variety of strategies for solving problems, they will become more flexible in their thinking and reasoning.

There is a strong connection between the problems in this series and the language arts—reading, writing, listening, and speaking. Careful reading of a word problem is often as important as mathematical skills for successfully solving the problem. It is critical that students
1) read the problem carefully,
2) find out what they are being asked to do,
3) solve the problem, and
4) determine whether or not the answer makes sense.

What's in This Book?

This book contains six sections, each of which focuses on a specific aspect of the problem-solving process and is designed to strengthen a particular reasoning skill.

Section 1: What Number Makes Sense?

This section contains problems and solutions from which numerical data has been removed. Students choose from a list of numbers to fill in the blanks so that the problems and solutions make sense.

Section 2: What's Wrong?

In this section students are given problems with solutions that contain errors in reasoning. The students identify the errors in reasoning and find the correct solutions to the problems.

Section 3: What Would You Do?

This section features open-ended problem situations. In each case, students solve the problem based upon their experiences, knowledge of the situation, and individual preference and then support their solutions.

Section 4: What Questions Can You Answer?

This section contains mathematical settings with numerical data. Students generate a list of questions that can be answered based on the data and then answer at least one of their questions.

Section 5: What's Missing?

Each problem in this section is missing data required to solve the problem. Students identify what is missing, supply appropriate data, and then solve the problem.

Section 6: What's the Question if You Know the Answer?

This section contains problem situations that include data, but no questions. Students are given several possible answers for which they must supply appropriate questions.

How to Use This Book

Each section begins with a teaching lesson that walks students through a problem similar to the rest of the problems in the section. Suggested questions are provided. Responses generated in discussion during the teaching lesson allow students an opportunity to share their thinking and listen to the thinking of their peers. These discussions help students clarify their understanding of the process for solving the problems in the section.

The teaching lessons are designed to guide students as they are learning procedures. Depending on the needs of your students, you may also want to consider using other problems in a section for whole-group lessons. A great deal of interesting dialogue and thoughtful questioning can occur during these whole-class lessons.

The problems in this book can be used in a variety of ways.

Class Opener or Warm up

Present the problem as an opening exercise to involve students in a discussion that can carry over into the day's lesson.

Class Closer

If there are a few minutes left at the end of a class period, introduce a problem in class and assign it as a homework or a family activity. Have students discuss the work at the beginning of the next day.

Small-group or Partners Activity

After you have introduced a section with the teaching lesson, most students will be able to solve the remaining problems with a partner or in a small group. Working in this way, students can share their thinking with their peers and get important feedback.

Individual Activity

After students have participated in the teaching lesson and worked with a partner or small group, many will be ready to solve additional problems individually. The ability to work these problems independently may vary from student to student.

Assessment

Suggested answers to problems in this book can be found at the end of each section. However, you might prefer using a rubric to evaluate students' reasoning. You might even decide to check one section, or certain problems within a section, using the answer key and to assess other sections or problems within a section using a rubric.

A rubric is helpful in assessing a student's mathematical proficiency in relationship to specific criteria. A rubric can also help to more reliably assess complex student work. It can be used to evaluate various dimensions of mathematical activity such as problem solving, communication, use of mathematical language, reasoning, and number sense.

© Creative Publications 0-7622-1350-7

The following general 3-point rubric can be used with any problem in any section of this book. If you prefer, feel free to develop your own rubric to provide for a more specific assessment. When using a rubric, it is recommended that you discuss the criteria with your students ahead of time. Doing so will help students to understand what a complete response should include and will encourage them to take time to reflect on their answers.

3	The student accomplishes the purpose of the question or task. Understanding of the mathematics in the task is demonstrated and the student is able to communicate his reasoning.
2	The student partially accomplishes the purpose of the question or task. Understanding of the mathematics may not be complete OR the student may not be able to communicate his reasoning adequately.
1	The student is not able to accomplish the purpose of the question or task. Understanding of the mathematics is fragmented and the communication is vague or incomplete.

Section 1

What Number Makes Sense?

IN THIS SECTION, STUDENTS ARE PRESENTED with problem situations from which numerical data is missing. A set of numbers is provided and students determine where to place each number so the situation makes sense.

It is suggested that the teaching problem that follows be used as a whole-class activity.

The procedures outlined in the teaching problem will help students understand how to

a) carefully read the numerical situation,

b) decide which numbers to place in each blank,

c) determine whether the numbers they chose make sense.

The group interaction that occurs during the lesson will provide an opportunity for students to explain their thinking.

Consider having students work the first few problems that follow the teaching problem either with a partner or in a small group. After they have had a chance to become comfortable working with this type of problem, students can complete the remaining problems independently.

As they work through the exercises here, students practice computation and increase their repertoire of problem-solving skills. Reasoning skills are improved as students are exposed to a variety of ways to solve a problem. Be sure to engage students in a class discussion after each problem has been completed so they can hear ways of solving problems that differ from their own.

Mathematical Skills
....

Teaching Problem
Multiplication, Addition

Problem 1
Addition, Multiplication

Problem 2
Multiplication, Addition

Problem 3
Addition, Subtraction

Problem 4
Division, Multiplication

Problem 5
Addition, Subtraction,
Multiplication

Problem 6
Time, Addition,
Multiplication

Problem 7
Money, Multiplication,
Subtraction

Problem 8
Addition, Multiplication

Problem 9
Money, Multiplication,
Subtraction

Problem 10
Time, Temperature,
Subtraction

Farm Animals

Teaching Goal

After participating in this lesson, students will be able to solve the problem by identifying and accurately placing the missing information. Students will also be able to explain their reasoning and defend their answers.

Problem

> A farmer has _____ animals on his farm.
> Some of them are cows and some are turkeys.
> Altogether the animals have _____ legs. Each
> cow has 4 legs and each turkey has 2 legs. The
> farmer has _____ cows and _____ turkeys.
>
> 15   20   35   100

Teaching Plan

1. Present the problem to the students.

2. Have students read the problem individually or read it together as a class.

3. Ask students to think about the problem. Ask what they need to do to solve the problem.

4. Ask students what information is given in the problem that helps them solve it. For example, does the term "altogether" provide any clues?

5. Have the students put the numbers in the blanks where they fit best.

 © Creative Publications 0-7622-1350-7

6. Have students read the problem again to see if their answers make sense.

7. Lead a whole group discussion. Consider using the following questions as part of the discussion:

How many animals does the farmer have? 35 animals

How many legs do the animals have altogether? 100 legs

How many cows does the farmer have? 15 cows

How many turkeys does the farmer have? 20 turkeys

Explain how you know you put the numbers in the correct blanks.

Would it be possible in this problem for the number of cows to be 20 and the number of turkeys to be 15? Why or Why not? No. The total number of legs would exceed the greatest of the given choices.

What strategy did you use?

Do you think your strategy will work for other problems of this kind?

....

This think and check problem solving process, along with class discussion allows students to use, extend, and communicate their reasoning and logic skills.

Name

Problem 1 **Photo Album**

James bought a new photo album.

The album contains _____ pages.

Each page can hold _____ photos.

If James has _____ photos to

mount, he will use _____ pages.

4 50 200 240

1. First, read the problem.

2. Look at the numbers in the box.

3. Put the numbers in the blanks where you think they fit best.

4. Read the problem again. Do the numbers make sense?

5. Explain how you know you have the numbers in the correct blanks.

_____

_____

_____

_____

_____

Name

....

Problem 2 **State Fair**

The State Fair opened at _____ a.m. During the

first 30 minutes _____ people arrived. Thirty minutes

later, the ticket taker noticed that the crowd at

the fairgrounds had tripled to _____ people.

During the next half-hour 100 more tickets were sold.

Altogether, _____ people had entered the fairgrounds.

9   18   54   154

1. First, read the problem.

2. Look at the numbers in the box.

3. Put the numbers in the blanks where you think they fit best.

4. Read the problem again. Do the numbers make sense?

5. Explain how you know you have the numbers in the correct blanks.

_____

_____

_____

Section ❶ **What Number Makes Sense?**

Name
....

Problem 3 **PTA Meeting**

The PTA is expecting _____ members at its October

meeting at Mrs. Rodriguez's house. Mrs. Rodriguez

has _____ chairs. She needs _____ more chairs

so that everyone can sit down. Her neighbor will

bring _____ chairs. Her son will bring _____ more

chair. Then she will be ready for the meeting.

1   3   4   31   35

1. First, read the problem.

2. Look at the numbers in the box.

3. Put the numbers in the blanks where you think they fit best.

4. Read the problem again. Do the numbers make sense?

5. Explain how you know you have the numbers in the correct blanks.

_____

_____

_____

_____

6 **Roads to Reasoning** | Grade 4

© Creative Publications 0-7622-1350-7

Problem 4 **Gas Mileage**

The Miller family went on a weekend camping trip in their van. They traveled a total of _____ miles. Mr. Miller said the van used _____ gallons of gasoline. The family averaged _____ miles per gallon of gas.

15	30	450

1. First, read the problem.

2. Look at the numbers in the box.

3. Put the numbers in the blanks where you think they fit best.

4. Read the problem again. Do the numbers make sense?

5. Explain how you know you have the numbers in the correct blanks.

_____

_____

_____

_____

Problem 5 **New Baby**

Molly's new baby sister was born on

May _____ and weighed 8 pounds

and 6 ounces. After 2 months, she

weighed _____ pounds and _____

ounces. The baby had gained _____

ounces since she was born.

16 ounces = 1 pound

4	9	14	27

1. First, read the problem.

2. Look at the numbers in the box.

3. Put the numbers in the blanks where you think they fit best.

4. Read the problem again. Do the numbers make sense?

5. Explain how you know you have the numbers in the correct blanks.

_____

_____

_____

_____

Name
....

Problem 6 **Vegetable Stand**

Lorna and Chris work at a roadside stand selling

vegetables they grow in their garden. They keep

the stand open six days a week. Lorna works from

_____ a.m. to _____ p.m. Chris works from

_____ noon to _____ p.m. Together, Lorna

and Chris work a total of _____ hours per week.

1	4	8	12	54

1. First, read the problem.

2. Look at the numbers in the box.

3. Put the numbers in the blanks where you think they fit best.

4. Read the problem again. Do the numbers make sense?

5. Explain how you know you have the numbers in the correct blanks.

_____

_____

_____

Problem 7 **Drama Club Plays**

There are _____ members in the Drama Club.

At the beginning of the school year, each member

of the club collected _____ dollars for props.

The club spent _____ dollars on the first play.

They have _____ dollars left for the other plays.

10	25	75	175

1. First, read the problem.

2. Look at the numbers in the box.

3. Put the numbers in the blanks where you think they fit best.

4. Read the problem again. Do the numbers make sense?

5. Explain how you know you have the numbers in the correct blanks.

_____

_____

_____

Problem 8 **Odometer Readings**

Terry and Sandy have new cars.

Terry already has _____ miles on his odometer.

Sandy has only _____ miles on hers.

Terry and Sandy each drive _____ miles a week.

It will take _____ weeks for Terry's odometer

to read twice that of Sandy's.

6	**100**	**600**	**1800**

1. First, read the problem.

2. Look at the numbers in the box.

3. Put the numbers in the blanks where you think they fit best.

4. Read the problem again. Do the numbers make sense?

5. Explain how you know you have the numbers in the correct blanks.

_____

_____

_____

Problem 9 **Photo Processing**

Judy took _____ rolls of film to the

Rapid Photo Shop to have them processed.

Each roll costs _____. If she gives

the shopkeeper _____, she should

receive _____ in change.

2	$6.50	$6.75	$20.00

1. First, read the problem.

2. Look at the numbers in the box.

3. Put the numbers in the blanks where you think they fit best.

4. Read the problem again. Do the numbers make sense?

5. Explain how you know you have the numbers in the correct blanks.

_____

_____

_____

_____

   © Creative Publications 0-7622-1350-7

Problem 10 **Winter Vacation**

For their winter vacation the Lee family flew from

Philadelphia, Pennsylvania to Orlando, Florida.

They left Philadelphia, where the temperature was

_____ degrees, at _____ a.m. When they

landed in Orlando, it was _____ p.m. and the

temperature was _____ degrees. The difference

in temperature was _____ degrees.

37	41	78	1:45	11:15

1. First, read the problem.

2. Look at the numbers in the box.

3. Put the numbers in the blanks where you think they fit best.

4. Read the problem again. Do the numbers make sense?

5. Explain how you know you have the numbers in the correct blanks.

_____

_____

_____

Answer Key

Problem 1: Photo Album
240 pages, 4 photos, 200 photos,
50 pages

Problem 2: State Fair
9 a.m., 18 people, 54 people,
154 people

Problem 3: PTA Meeting
35 members, 31 chairs, 4 more,
3 chairs, 1 more chair

Problem 4: Gas Mileage
450 miles, 30 gallons,
15 miles per gallon
or 15 gallons, 30 miles per gallon

Problem 5: New Baby
27th, 9 pounds, 4 ounces,
14 ounces

Problem 6: Vegetable Stand
8 a.m., 1 p.m., 12 noon, 4 p.m.,
54 hours

Problem 7: Drama Club Plays
25 members, 10 dollars, 75 dollars,
175 dollars

Problem 8: Odometer Readings
1,800 miles, 600 miles,
100 miles per week, 6 weeks

Problem 9: Photo Processing
2 rolls, $6.75, 20-dollar bill, $6.50

Problem 10: Winter Vacation
37 degrees, 11:15 a.m., 1:45 p.m.,
78 degrees, 41 degrees
or 41 degrees, 11:15 a.m.,
1:45 p.m., 78 degrees, 37 degrees

Assessment Note
Student work on any of the
problems in this section can be
assessed using the 3-step rubric
on page ix.

Section 2 What's Wrong?

EACH PROBLEM THAT IS PRESENTED in this section has been solved, but the solution is incorrect. An error has been made either in concept, interpretation, or computation. Students must identify the error that was made and find the correct solution to the problem.

It is recommended that the teaching problem that follows be used as a whole-class activity.

The procedures outlined in the teaching problem will take students through the process of

a) finding the correct solution to the problem,

b) identifying the error that was made.

Consider having students work the first few problems that follow the teaching problem either with a partner or in a small group. This will provide an opportunity for them to become comfortable working with this type of problem. The remaining pages might then be assigned for students to complete independently.

This section deals with error analysis. Each exercise offers an effective means for students to practice computation skills within a problem-solving context. Different strategies such as drawing diagrams or pictures, writing an equation, or creating a table or graph may be used to solve problems. By engaging in class discussion after a problem has been completed, students will be able to hear ways of solving problems that differ from their own. The group interaction that occurs during these discussions often leads to deeper mathematical understanding.

Mathematical Skills

....

Teaching Problem
Fractions, Division

Problem 1
Number Sense, Counting on

Problem 2
Time, Addition

Problem 3
Multiplication, Division

Problem 4
Fractions

Problem 5
Decimals, Division

Problem 6
Time, Computation

Problem 7
Drawing a Diagram,
Multiplication, Fractions,
Division

Problem 8
Variables, Addition,
Subtraction

Problem 9
Addition, Subtraction,
Division

Problem 10
Drawing a Diagram,
Computation

Spirit Day

Teaching Goal

After participating in this lesson, students will be able to identify a reasoning error presented in the problem. Students will also choose a representation, either visual or numerical, and use it to solve the problem.

Problem

> For Spirit Day, Mrs. Wiggins ordered 256 hats for four classes. When the hats arrived, she asked each class representative to come to her office and take $\frac{1}{4}$ of the hats. Sandy arrived first and took $\frac{1}{4}$ of the hats. Next, Mitchell arrived and took $\frac{1}{4}$ of the hats that were there. Then, Lauren came and took $\frac{1}{4}$ of the hats that were left. Finally, Carlos came and took $\frac{1}{4}$ of the hats that were there. The next morning Mrs. Wiggins arrived and was surprised to find 81 hats in her office. Explain what happened.

Teaching Plan

1. Present the problem to the students.

2. Have students read the problem.

3. Lead a whole group discussion. Consider using the following questions as part of the discussion:

   How many hats should each of the classes have received?
   $\frac{1}{4}$ of 256 or 64

   How many hats did Sandy take? $\frac{1}{4}$ of 256 or 64

   How many hats were now left? $256 - 64$ or 192

How many hats did Mitchell take? $\frac{1}{4}$ of 192 or 48

How many hats were now left? $192 - 48 = 144$

How many hats did Lauren take? $\frac{1}{4}$ of $144 = 36$

How many hats were now left? $144 - 36 = 108$

How many hats did Carlos take? $\frac{1}{4}$ of $108 = 27$

How many hats were now left? $108 - 27 = 81$

Why did each class rep take a different number of hats? Each took $\frac{1}{4}$ of a different number.

How could Mrs. Wiggins have made the directions more clear?

Explain your strategy.

Does anyone have a different strategy?

....

You may wish to encourage students to use a specific representation to solve the different problems in this section. You may also have them try to use multiple representations such as a drawing and using an equation to solve one or more of the problems.

Problem 1 **Bridge Tolls**

Mr. Costello uses coupons to pay tolls for
the bridge he crosses on his way to work.
Each coupon book has 20 coupons. The
coupons are numbered 1 to 20. Today
Mr. Costello used coupon number 11. He
reasons that since he has numbers 12
through 20 left, he has 8 more coupons.

Mr. Costello's thinking ▶ $20 - 12 = 8$

There is something wrong with Mr. Costello's thinking.

1. Show how you would find how many coupons are left.

2. Explain the mistake in Mr. Costello's thinking.

_____

_____

Name

....

Problem 2 **Bus Times**

Buses leave Philadelphia for New York
City every half-hour from 6:45 a.m. until
8:00 p.m. Theresa thinks that if she
leaves Philadelphia at 9:45 a.m., she
will be taking the 6th bus of the day.

Theresa's thinking ▶

6:45 to 9:45 is 3 hours
3 × 2 = 6

There is something wrong with Theresa's thinking.

1. Show how you would find which bus Theresa will take if she leaves at 9:45.

2. Explain the mistake in Theresa's thinking.

_____

_____

Problem 3 **Picnic Seating**

There are 61 students attending the school picnic.
Eight students can sit around the large picnic
tables. The small tables seat four students. There
are only six large tables and they are all full.
Carla said she thought that the rest of the children
could sit at three small tables.

Carla's thinking ▶ $6 \times 8 = 48$

$$61 - 48 = 13$$

$$13 \div 4 = 3.25$$

There is something wrong with Carla's thinking.

1. Show how you would find how many small tables are needed.

2. Explain the mistake in Carla's thinking.

_____

_____

Name
....

Problem 4 **Egypt Tour**

A group of 120 tourists were on a tour of Egypt. Half of the group went to see the pyramids. Of these, $\frac{3}{4}$ took pictures. The tour guide figured that 90 people took pictures.

The tour guide's thinking ▶

$$\frac{3}{4} \times 120 = 90$$

There is something wrong with the tour guide's thinking.

1. Show how you would find how many people took pictures at the pyramids.

2. Explain the mistake in the tour guide's thinking.

_____

_____

Problem 5 **Taxi Trip**

A taxi charges \$1.50 for the first $\frac{1}{4}$-mile and \$0.75 for each additional quarter mile. George paid \$6.00 for his taxi ride. He thought his trip must have been $1\frac{1}{2}$ miles long.

George's thinking ▶
$$\$6.00 - \$1.50 = \$4.50$$
$$\$4.50 \div \$0.75 = 6$$
$$6 \times \frac{1}{4} = 1\frac{1}{2}$$

There is something wrong with George's thinking.

1. Show how you would find how long George's trip was.

2. Explain the mistake in George's thinking.

_____

_____

_____

© Creative Publications 0-7622-1350-7

Problem 6 **Daily Exercise**

Cameron exercises 15 minutes every morning and 35 minutes every afternoon. When asked how much time she spent exercising each week, Cameron replied, "3 and $\frac{1}{2}$ hours."

Cameron's thinking ▶

$$15 + 35 = 50 \text{ minutes per day}$$
$$50 \times 7 = 350 \text{ minutes per week}$$
$$350 \div 100 = 3\frac{1}{2} \text{ hours per week}$$

There is something wrong with Cameron's thinking.

1. Show how you would find how long Cameron exercised each week.

2. Explain the mistake in Cameron's thinking.

_____

_____

Problem 7 **Cutting Costs**

It costs $14.00 to cut a 10-foot board into 8 equal

parts. Kris figures it would cost exactly one-half,

or $7.00, to cut a 5-foot board into 4 equal parts.

Kris's thinking ▶

> The 5-foot board is half as long as the 10-foot board.
> Four equal parts are half of 8 equal parts.
> $14.00 ÷ 2 = $7.00

There is something wrong with Kris's thinking.

1. Show how you would find how much it would cost to cut

a 5-foot board into 4 equal parts.

2. Explain the mistake in Kris's thinking.

_____

_____

Name

....

Problem 8 **Mystery Sum**

The following problem was given during
a math class: The sum of two numbers is 15.
One of the numbers is 9. What is the other
number? Raina thinks the answer is 24.

Raina's thinking ▶ **15 + 9 = 24**

There is something wrong with Raina's thinking.

1. Show how you would find the answer to the problem.

```

```

2. Explain the mistake in Raina's thinking.

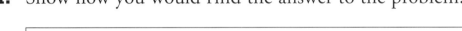

_____

_____

Problem 9 **Sharing Expenses**

Mrs. Rios and Mrs. Chun went on a business trip
together. They decided to share all their expenses equally.
Mrs. Rios spent $125.00. Mrs. Chun spent $85.00.

Mrs. Rios's thinking ▶

$$\$125.00 - \$85.00 = \$40.00$$
Mrs. Chun owes $40.00.

There is something wrong with Mrs. Rios's thinking.

1. Show how you would find the answer to the problem.

2. Explain the mistake in Mrs. Rios's thinking.

_____

_____

Name
....

Problem 10 **Fence Building**

Mark is installing a 40-foot fence
along the back of his property line.
He ordered 4,10-foot sections of fence
and 4 posts. When the materials arrived
he began to install the fence and
found he couldn't finish the job.

Mark's thinking ▶ $40 \div 10 = 4$ sections

There is something wrong with Mark's thinking.

1. Show how you would find how many posts to order.

2. Explain the mistake in Mark's thinking.

_____

_____

Answer Key

Problem 1: Bridge Tolls

The correct answer is 9 coupons. Students may solve by counting out tickets, or using a visual representation. Mr. Costello subtracted 12 from 20; he did not include the coupon number 12. Students may start at 12 and count up to 20.

Problem 2: Bus Times

Theresa will take the 7th bus. Students might start with 6:45 and add on $\frac{1}{2}$ hour until they get to 9:45. Theresa did not include the bus that left at 6:45.

Problem 3: Picnic Seating

Carla's calculations are correct. The error lies in the rounding down to 3. A fourth table is needed to seat everyone.

Problem 4: Egypt Tour

Students should calculate $\frac{1}{2} \times 120 = 60$ and $\frac{3}{4} \times 60 = 45$ people. The tour guide did not take into account that only half of the 120 total people went to see the pyramids.

Problem 5: Taxi Trip

The trip was actually $1\frac{3}{4}$ miles. George forgot to add the initial $\frac{1}{4}$-mile.

Problem 6: Daily Exercise

The correct answer is $5\frac{5}{6}$ hours *or* 5 hr. 50 min. The incorrect solution stems from the misconception that there are 100 minutes in an hour instead of 60.

Problem 7: Cutting Costs

Students should draw a model to represent each situation:

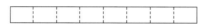

7 cuts yields 8 pieces;
$14.00 ÷ 7 cuts = $2.00 per cut.

3 cuts yields 4 pieces;
3 cuts at $2.00 each = $6.00.

Problem 8: Mystery Sum

Students may set up equations like $9 + x = 15$ or $15 - 9 = x$ to find that the other number is 6. Raina added the sum and the given addend together instead of finding the missing addend.

Problem 9: Sharing Expenses

Mrs. Chun should give Mrs. Rios $20.00. Each person's share is actually $105.00 since together their expenses were $125.00 + $85.00 or $210.00 and $210.00 ÷ 2 is $105.00.

Problem 10: Fence Building

A drawing would show that Mark needs 5 posts, not 4. There has to be a post on both ends of the fence and 3 posts in between. Mark divided the total length of the fence by 10.

Assessment Note

Student work on any of the problems in this section can be assessed using the 3-point rubric on page ix.

Section 3   **What Would You Do?**

OPEN-ENDED PROBLEMS ARE PRESENTED in this section. In each case, after finding an answer, students are asked to support their solution.

These problems give students the opportunity to use their prior knowledge as a foundation on which to build and strengthen their skills. Both computation and problem-solving abilities are engaged.

Consider using the teaching problem format with the first few problems in the section. The next few might then be solved within small groups, and the remaining problems completed on an individual basis.

Group discussions about solutions provide an important forum for a valuable exchange of ideas. These discussions allow students to practice effective communication of their own mathematical thinking and to gain insights and understanding through listening to the solution strategies of others.

Mathematical Skills

Teaching Problem
Money, Addition, Subtraction

Problem 1
Computation

Problem 2
Computation

Problem 3
Fractions

Problem 4
Computation

Problem 5
Money, Addition

Problem 6
Addition, Subtraction, Fractions

Problem 7
Counting Methods

Problem 8
Money, Multiplication, Division

Problem 9
Probability

Problem 10
Money, Computation

Science Club Aquarium

Teaching Goal

After participating in this lesson, students see how they can apply their experiences, prior knowledge, and individual preferences to solve the problem. Students will also be able to support their answers using logic and reasoning.

Problem

The students in the Science Club are setting up an aquarium in the science room. The chart below shows the price of items at the pet store. They have $40.00 to spend.

Aquarium Supplies

Tank	$8.00 each
Colored pebbles	$1.50 per bag
Plants	$0.50 each
Fish food	$2.50 a box
Heater	$7.25 each
Castle ornament	$2.50 each
Pump and filter	$10.00

Goldfish

Black Moor	$2.50 each
Gold Moor	$2.25 each
Veiltails	$3.50 each
Orange and White	$2.00 each
Common	$0.50 each
Calico	$2.25 each

Teaching Plan

1. Present the problem to the students.

2. Have the students read the problem.

3. Lead a whole group discussion. Consider using the following questions as part of the discussion:

Which items would you choose?

In this problem, students may want to make two lists: one for supplies and one for the fish.

Explain the choices you made.

Some supplies are necessary. For example, the students must have a tank, fish, and some fish food. A heater is not usually needed for goldfish, and a pump and filter are optional.

....

Since the problems in this section are somewhat open-ended, there may be a variety of strategies and solutions. It is important to encourage the students to choose a solution that they can defend.

Name

....

Problem 1 **Football Season**

Harrison High School's football team
plays an eight-game schedule.
You can buy a season ticket for $60.00
or individual tickets for $9.00.
What would you do?

1. Choose which way you would purchase the tickets. Is this the best value?

_____

_____

_____

2. Explain your reasoning for the choice you made.

_____

_____

_____

_____

_____

_____

Name
....

Problem 2 **Gift Certificate**

You have won a $100.00 gift certificate
at the Village Music Shop. You have
a VCR, a CD player, and a cassette
recorder at home. The costs for videos,
cassettes, and CDs are listed on the
sign. You want to spend as much
of your gift certificate as possible at
one time. What would you do?

Item	Cost
Videos	$19.00 each
Cassettes	$ 6.00 each
CDs	$14.00 each

1. How would you spend the gift certificate? Use the table to record your
choices and the total cost.

Item	Quantity	Cost	Subtotal
Videos			
Cassettes			
CDs			
		Total Cost	

2. Explain how you made your choices.

_____

_____

_____

Name

....

Problem 3 **Pizza Time**

You and two friends are just about to share
a pizza that is cut in three equal portions
as shown. Just as you were about to eat,
another friend joins the group. How will you
divide the pizza to share it equally?

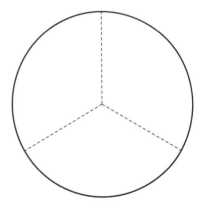

1. Show how you would divide the pizza equally for four people.

2. Explain your reasoning.

_____

_____

_____

_____

_____

Problem 4 **Library Choices**

You have just discovered a library book that you forgot to return. It is 23 days overdue. The fine for overdue books is 20 cents a day for the first 10 days and 10 cents a day for the remaining days. The librarian said that if you wish, you could buy the book for $5.00 instead of paying the fine.

1. Which payment method would you choose?

_____

2. Which is the better value?

_____

3. Explain how you made your choices in question 1.

_____

_____

_____

_____

Name
....

Problem 5 **Museum Gift Shop**

You have $7.25 to spend at the museum gift shop. The list shows the prices of the items that you can purchase.

Item	Cost
Dinosaur kit	$3.50
Whale model	$2.95
Key ring	$0.85
Indian feather eraser	$0.50
Rubber snake	$1.15
Bird whistle	$1.95
Animal stickers	$0.75

1. Which items would you choose to buy? Show your choices with the total cost.

Item	Cost
1.	
2.	
3.	
4.	
5.	
Total	

2 Explain how you made your choices in question 1.

_____

_____

Name
....

Problem 6 **Camping Trip**

You are packing a backpack
to take on a camping trip.
You may take up to 15 pounds.
Use the list to decide what
you will take.

Item	Weight
Portable CD player	$2\frac{1}{2}$ pounds
CDs	$\frac{1}{4}$ pound each
Lantern	3 pounds
Books	1 pound each
Box of snacks	1 pound
Flashlight	1 pound
Baseball mitt	$1\frac{1}{2}$ pounds
Baseball	$\frac{1}{2}$ pound
Sleeping bag	5 pounds

1. Fill in the table with the choices
you make.

Item	Weight
1.	
2.	
3.	
4.	
5.	
Total	

2. Explain how you made your choices.

_____

_____

Problem 7 **Table Tennis Tournament**

You are in charge of setting up
the table tennis tournament for
the After School Club. There are
6 club members competing. Each
member should play every other
member once.

1. Create a schedule for the tournament.

2. Explain your reasoning.

_____

_____

_____

Name ....

Problem 8 **Picnic Supplies**

Gabe needed some supplies for the class picnic.
There will be approximately 50 people at the
picnic. Gabe did some comparison shopping at
the local market and the discount store. The
chart shows what he found.

Item	Local Market	Discount Store
8-ounce cups	12 for $1.00	100 for $6.00
Paper dinner plates	8 for $2.00	100 for $15.00
Paper napkins	50 for $0.99	250 for $1.95
Assorted plastic utensils	40 for $1.00	210 for $3.50

1. At which store should Gabe purchase the picnic supplies?

8-ounce cups _____

Paper dinner plates _____

Paper napkins _____

Plastic untensils _____

2. In which store will he get the best value?_____

3. Explain why you made your choices in question 1.

_____

_____

Name
....

Problem 9 **Game Time**

Each group in your class is making
up a game to be played during recess
on rainy days. Your group has been
assigned the task of designing
a spinner game. You need to
make up a name for your game,
determine the rules, and decide
how a person wins or loses.

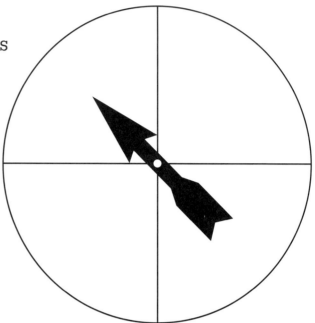

1. Give the name and rules of the game you have designed.

_____

_____

_____

_____

2. Describe the scoring and how someone wins or loses the game.

_____

_____

_____

Name
....

Problem 10 **Transportation Choices**

You use public transportation to go to and from school each day.
The Urban Transportation Company has 3 plans for commuters.

Plan 1	Tokens good for 1 ride cost $1.60 each.
Plan 2	A weekly pass good for any number of rides during one week costs $17.25.
Plan 3	A monthly pass good for any number of rides during one month costs $45.00.

1. Which plan would you choose?

_____

2. Which is the better value?

_____

3. Explain how you made your choice.

_____

_____

_____

_____

Answer Key

Problems 1–10
Answers will vary. Be sure to discuss individual solutions.

Assessment Note
Student work on any of the problems in this section can be assessed using the 3-point rubric on page ix.

Section 4 What Questions Can You Answer?

Section 4

IN THIS SECTION, STUDENTS ARE PRESENTED with situations that include numerical data and are asked to generate questions that can be answered from the data. There is a natural integration of language arts and mathematics as students analyze information, formulate and record their questions, and then find the answers to the questions they've created.

It is recommended that the teaching problem that follows be used as a whole-class activity.

The procedures outlined in the teaching problem will help students understand how to

a) identify the information that is given in the problem,

b) determine what questions can be answered from the data,

c) find a solution and an answer to the questions posed.

Consider having students work the first few problems that follow the teaching problem with a partner or in small groups. This will allow them to brainstorm ideas to generate as many questions as possible. They can select their best questions to record on the student page and then work together to find the solutions. The remaining problems might then be assigned for students to work independently.

After students have completed working on a problem, be sure to discuss the questions generated as well as the answers. Such discussion can provide a valuable opportunity for students to hear the variety of questions posed.

Mathematical Skills

....

Teaching Problem
Multiplication, Division

Problem 1
Addition, Subtraction, Drawing a Diagram

Problem 2
Addition, Subtraction

Problem 3
Calendar

Problem 4
Addition, Multiplication, Money, Subtraction

Problem 5
Data Analysis, Time, Money, Multiplication

Problem 6
Logic, Addition, Subtraction

Problem 7
Addition, Subtraction, Measurement

Problem 8
Addition, Time

Problem 9
Data Analysis, Addition, Subtraction

Problem 10
Elapsed Time, Computation

The Comic Strip

Teaching Goal

After participating in this lesson, students should be able to see the breadth and depth of questions that can be constructed with given data. They should also be able to understand how to find the answers to the questions they pose.

Problem

Briana draws a cartoon strip for the local newspaper. The same number of frames appears each day. In March she drew 80 frames, enough for 20 days. In April, she drew 120 frames in just 40 hours.

Teaching Plan

1. Write the above information on the overhead projector, chalkboard, or white board.

2. Ask the students to read the information.

3. Lead a discussion with the whole class using the following questions as part of the discussion.

   What does the term "frame" mean when referring to a comic strip?

   If possible, have a couple of strips from the newspaper available for students to view.

   What information are you given? The same number of frames appear in the paper each day. In March Briana drew 80 frames which was enough for 20 days. In April she drew 120 frames in 40 hours.

   You may want to underline the information on the board as students volunteer it, or write it in a separate place on the board.

When you see numbers and a problem like this, the teacher usually asks some questions about the numbers. Today you are going to get a chance to be the teacher and think of some questions that could be answered with the given information. Can you think of one?

One question that students may suggest is, "How many frames appear each day?" Record that question on the board and continue asking for questions.

4. Encourage students to generate questions where they will need to perform mathematical calculations. Possible questions where mathematical calculations are required are:

   How many frames did Briana draw in March and April?

   About how long does it take Briana to draw one frame?

   How many frames could Briana draw in 20 hours?

5. After your students have generated an interesting variety of questions, have them create a solution and find the answer for each.

   How can we find out how many frames appear in the paper each day?

   How would you go about figuring how long it takes Briana to draw one frame?

   What strategy would you use to figure out how many frames Briana can draw in 20 hours?

   ....

   Almost all students will be able to achieve some level of success with this lesson. The sophistication of questions posed depends on the developmental level of each student.

Section 4

Problem 1 **The Road to Dover**

A straight road from Alton to Dover is 82 miles
long. It passes through Carlton and Benham.
It is 20 miles from Alton to Canton and 41 miles
from Alton to Benham.

Write two questions you can answer about the distances between the cities
on the road to Dover.

1. _____

_____

_____

2. _____

_____

_____

3. Find the answer to your first question. Show your work.

_____

_____

_____

_____

Name

....

Problem 2 **The Stamp Collection**

Toshi and Jeff both have a stamp collection. Toshi has 155 stamps from the United States and 115 foreign stamps. Jeff has 215 stamps from the United States and 85 foreign stamps.

Write two questions you can answer about the boys' stamp collections.

1. _____

_____

_____

2. _____

_____

_____

3. Find the answer to your first question. Show your work.

_____

_____

_____

Name
....

Problem 3 **November Calendar**

Sunday	Monday	Tuesday	Wednesday	Thursday	Friday	Saturday
			1	2	3	4
5	6	7 Election Day	8	9	10	11 Veteran's Day
12	13	14	15	16	17	18
19	20	21	22	23 Thanksgiving Day	24	25
26	27	28	29	30		

Write two questions you can answer about this calendar.

1. _____

_____

2. _____

_____

3. Find the answer to your first question. Show your work.

_____

_____

© Creative Publications 0-7622-1350-7

Name
....

Problem 4 **The Book Fair**

Mrs. Duncan is sorting books for
the book fair. She has 31 hardcover books,
22 softcover books and 39 magazines.
Hardcover books sell for $7.00, softcover
books sell for $3.50, and magazines
sell for $1.50.

Write two questions you can answer about the books and magazines
for sale at the book fair.

1. _____

_____

_____

2. _____

_____

_____

3. Find the answer to your first question. Show your work.

_____

_____

_____

Problem 5 **Mario's Deli**

This is a table showing the weekend
work schedule at Mario's Deli.
Each person earns $6.00 an hour.

	Friday	**Saturday**
9:30 a.m.– 1:30 p.m.	Lynn	Chun
12:30 p.m.–6:30 p.m.	Alisha	Matthew
9:30 a.m.–4:30 p.m.	Rasheed	Marie
4:30 p.m.–9:30 p.m.	Shawn	Kaya

Write two questions you can answer about the work schedule.

1. _____

_____

2. _____

_____

3. Find the answer to your first question. Show your work.

_____

_____

_____

Problem 6 **Students' Heights**

Alisa is 39 inches tall. Haru is 21 inches
taller than Alisa. Darnell is 31 inches taller than
Alisa. Peter is 12 inches shorter than Haru.

Write two questions you can answer about the students' heights.

1. _____

_____

_____

2. _____

_____

_____

3. Find the answer to your first question. Show your work.

_____

_____

_____

_____

Problem 7 **The Rectangle**

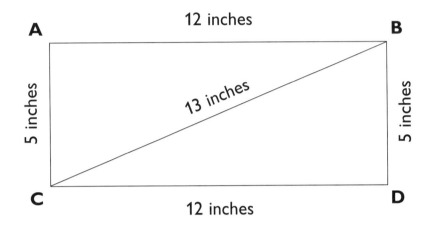

Write two questions you can answer about the rectangle.

1. _____

_____

2. _____

_____

3. Find the answer to your first question. Show your work.

_____

_____

_____

_____

© Creative Publications 0-7622-1350-7

Name
....

Problem 8 **The Train Trip**

A train leaves Philadelphia at 1:00 p.m.

It arrives in Trenton, a distance of 30 miles, at 1:30.

It then proceeds to Newark, which is 55 miles from Trenton.

It arrives there at 2:30. It leaves for New York at 2:40.

The final leg of the trip to New York is 15 miles.

It takes the train 20 minutes to complete that leg.

Write two questions you can answer about the train trip.

1. _____

_____

2. _____

_____

3. Find the answer to your first question. Show your work.

_____

_____

_____

_____

Name
....

Problem 9 **The Book Sale**

Mrs. Leary's fourth grade class is collecting
books for the school book sale. The graph
shows the number of books the class collected
each day for one week.

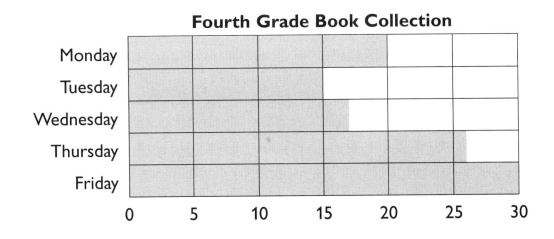

Fourth Grade Book Collection

Write two questions you can answer about the graph.

1. _____

_____

2. _____

_____

3. Find the answer to your first question. Show your work.

_____

_____

Name
....

Problem 10 **Department Store**

Marla works in a department store.

Her workday is from 9:00 a.m. until 4:30 p.m.

She has a lunch break from 12:00 until 12:45.

Yesterday she left home at 8:00 a.m. and

arrived at the store at 8:45 a.m. She left the

store at 4:45 p.m. and arrived home at 5:30 p.m.

Write two questions you can answer about Marla's day.

1. _____

_____

2. _____

_____

3. Find the answer to your first question. Show your work.

_____

_____

_____

_____

Answer Key

In this section students write questions that can be answered with the information given. This answer key includes typical questions that may be written by students. Many other questions are possible.

Problem 1: The Road to Dover
Possible questions
How far is it from Carlton to Benham?

How far is it from Carlton to Dover?

How far is it from Benham to Dover?

Problem 2: The Stamp Collection
Possible questions
Together, how many stamps do Toshi and Jeff have?

How many foreign stamps do they have together?

How many more stamps does Jeff have than Toshi?

Problem 3: November Calendar
Possible questions
How many days are there between Veteran's Day and Thanksgiving Day?

How many Wednesdays are there in November?

What date is Election Day?

Problem 4: The Book Fair
Possible questions
If Mrs. Duncan sells all the hard cover books at the book fair, how much money will be earned?

If half of the soft cover books are sold at the book fair, how much money will be gained?

How many items are for sale at the book fair in all?

Problem 5: Mario's Deli
Possible questions
How many more hours do Alisha and Matthew work than Lynn and Chun?

How much money do Shawn and Kaya earn on their shifts?

How much money do Rasheed and Marie earn on their shifts?

Problem 6: Students' Heights
Possible questions
How tall is Haru?

How tall is Darnell?

How tall is Peter?

Problem 7: The Rectangle
Possible questions
What is the perimeter of the rectangle?

What is the area of the rectangle?

What is the perimeter of either triangle?

Problem 8: The Train Trip
Possible questions
How many miles is it from Philadelphia to New York?

How long does it take the train to go from Philadelphia to New York?

How many miles is it from Philadelphia to Newark?

Problem 9: The Book Sale
Possible questions
How many books were collected on Monday and Tuesday?

How many more books were collected on Thursday than Monday?

How many books were collected on all five days?

Problem 10: The Department Store
Possible questions
How many hours long is Marla's work day?

How many hours was she away from her home yesterday?

What is the difference between Marla's usual work day and the number of hours she was away from her home yesterday?

Assessment Note
Students' work on any of the problems in this section can be assessed using the 3-step rubric on page ix.

Section 5   What's Missing?

IN THIS SECTION, STUDENTS ARE PRESENTED with problems that cannot be solved because an important piece of information has been omitted. Students must identify what is missing, supply appropriate data, and then solve the problem.

It is recommended that the teaching problem that follows be used as a whole-class activity.

The procedures outlined in the teaching problem will help students understand how to

a) identify the question that is asked,

b) determine the piece of information that is missing,

c) supply a number or other data that will enable them to solve the problem.

After the teaching problem, it is suggested that students work with a partner or in a small group, especially for the initial lessons. Once the majority of students are comfortable with the procedures, the remaining problems can be worked independently.

Group discussion of problems throughout this section is important, even after students are working independently. Because there is a wide range of data that students can supply to solve each problem, interesting discussions based on the specific data chosen are possible. Each different piece of missing information supplied by a student produces a different problem.

Mathematical Skills

Teaching Problem
Addition, Subtraction

Problem 1
Addition

Problem 2
Multiplication

Problem 3
Elapsed Time, Addition

Problem 4
Logic, Addition

Problem 5
Addition, Multiplication

Problem 6
Elapsed Time, Addition, Multiplication

Problem 7
Multiplication, Money

Problem 8
Addition, Subtraction

Problem 9
Multiplication, Division

Problem 10
Addition, Multiplication, Money

Basketball Team

Teaching Goal

After participating in this lesson, students should be able to identify the missing piece of information that is preventing them from solving the problem. They should also be able to choose a number or other data that will enable them to solve the problem. They should understand that there is a range of possible numbers or data that could be used to solve the problem.

> Ryan, Eli, and Kareem are on the school basketball team. In last night's game, Ryan scored 10 points more than Eli and five points fewer than Kareem. How many points did each of the boys score?

Teaching Plan

1. Write the problem on the overhead projector, chalkboard, or whiteboard.

2. Have the students read the problem.

3. Lead a discussion with the whole class using the following questions as part of the discussion.

   What question is being asked? How many points did each boy score?

   What information do you know from the problem? Ryan scored 10 points more than Eli. Ryan scored 5 points fewer than Kareem.

Why can't you answer the question? It is not known how many points were scored by any of the boys.

Pick the number of points Eli might have scored and write it on a piece of paper.

Now figure out the number of points scored by Ryan and Kareem.

What number did you pick for Eli?

4. Discuss each number volunteered by a student and determine which ones work.

For example, **If Eli scored 10 points, how many points did Kareem score? Are you able to figure out the number of points each boy scored if we know the number of points scored by Ryan? Kareem?**

....

Repeat above procedure so that students will see that if they know the number of points scored by one boy, they can figure out the scores of the other two boys.

Name ....

Problem 1 **Tour Boats**

Tour boats take tourists to see the Statue of Liberty. One boat carries 125 people and another carries 175 people. A tour company added two more boats that carry more passengers than either of the first two. Both of the new boats carry the same number of passengers. How many people can go out to see the Statue of Liberty if all four boats are used?

1. What is the question? _____

_____

2. What information do you know from the problem? _____

_____

3. What else do you need to know to solve the problem? _____

_____

4. Pick a number that shows how many people each of the new boats might

be able to carry. _____

5. How many people would be able to see the Statue of Liberty if all

four boats were used for one trip? _____

Problem 2 **The Swim Meet**

Lily is practicing for the swim meet by swimming laps in the pool every day. Each lap is a total of 25 yards. Last week she practiced 4 days and swam the same number of laps each day. How many yards did she swim last week?

1. What is the question? _____

_____

2. What information do you know from the problem?

_____

_____

3. What else do you need to know to solve the problem? _____

_____

_____

4. Pick the number of laps that Lily might have swum each day. _____

5. How many yards would she have swum last week? _____

Name ....

Problem 3 **At the Beach**

While Andrew was at the beach, the temperature
rose three degrees every hour. He arrived at the beach
at 10:00 a.m. and left for home at 2:00 p.m.
What was the temperature when he left the beach?

1. What is the question? _____

_____

2. What information do you know from the problem?

_____

_____

3. What else do you need to know to solve the problem?

_____

_____

4. Pick a number that shows what the temperature might have been when

Andrew arrived at the beach. _____

5. What would the temperature have been when Andrew left the beach?

_____

Problem 4 **Football Season**

The Hawks, Eagles, and Falcons are football teams.
During the season, each of these teams played
one game against the other. The Eagles beat the
Hawks 14–7. The Eagles beat the Falcons 21–13.
The Hawks and Falcons played to a tie. What
is the total number of points scored by each team?

1. What is the question? _____

_____

2. What information do you know from the problem? _____

_____

3. What else do you need to know to solve the problem? _____

_____

4. Pick a number that shows how many points might have been scored in

the tie game between the Hawks and Falcons. _____

5. How many points were scored by each team in both of their games?

_____

Problem 5 **Movie Tickets**

Tickets to a local movie theater cost $7.50
for adults and $3.00 for children under 12.
Mr. and Mrs. Meyers took their children
to the movies on Saturday. How much did
they spend on tickets?

1. What is the question? _____

_____

2. What information do you know from the problem? _____

_____

_____

3. What else do you need to know to solve the problem? _____

_____

4. Pick a number that shows how many children might be in the

Meyers family. _____

5. How much would the Meyers family spend on movie tickets?

_____

© Creative Publications 0-7622-1350-7

Problem 6 **Parking Meter**

Mrs. Sanchez was shopping downtown. She
parked her car on the street by a parking meter.
The rates were $0.25 for each 15 minutes.
Mrs. Sanchez put seven quarters into the meter.
By what time does she need to return to her car?

1. What is the question? _____

_____

2. What information do you know from the problem? _____

_____

3. What else do you need to know to solve the problem?

_____

_____

4. Pick a time when Mrs. Sanchez might have parked her car.

_____

5. By what time would Mrs. Sanchez need to return to her car?

_____

Problem 7 **Sold Out Performance**

A small theater holds 125 people. During the
first week of February five performances were
scheduled. How much money was collected if
all five performances sold out?

1. What is the question? _____

_____

2. What information do you know from the problem?

_____

_____

3. What else do you need to know to solve the problem?

_____

_____

4. Pick a number that shows how much money might be charged for

each ticket. _____

5. How much money would be collected for the five performances?

_____

© Creative Publications 0-7622-1350-7

Problem 8 **The Spelling Bee**

Edison School, Lincoln School, and Franklin School each sent students to the spelling bee finals. The three schools sent a total of 28 students. Edison School sent twice as many as Lincoln School. How many students did each school send?

1. What is the question? _____

_____

2. What information do you know from the problem?

_____

_____

3. What else do you need to know to solve the problem?

_____

_____

4. Pick a number that shows how many students might have been sent

by either Edison or Lincoln School. _____

5. How many contestants would have been sent by each school?

_____

Name
....

Problem 9 **Muffins**

Lynn bought five packages of muffins for
her party. She spent $15.00 for the five
packages. How much did each muffin cost?

1. What is the question? _____

_____

2. What information do you know from the problem?

_____

_____

3. What else do you need to know to solve the problem? _____

_____

_____

4. Pick a number that shows how many muffins might have been

in each package. _____

5. How much would each muffin cost? _____

 © Creative Publications 0-7622-1350-7

Problem 10 **Postage Stamps**

Ivan purchased two sheets of postage stamps at the
post office. One sheet contained 20 stamps and the other
sheet contained more than the first one. If each stamp
costs 34 cents, how much did Ivan pay for the stamps?

1. What is the question? _____

_____

2. What information do you know from the problem?

_____

_____

3. What else do you need to know to solve the problem?

_____

_____

4. Pick a number that shows how many stamps might have been

on the second sheet. _____

5. How much would Ivan have to pay for the stamps? _____

Answer Key

The answers for #4 and #5 in each problem will vary depending on the data supplied by the student.

Problem 1: Tour Boats

1. How many people can go to see the Statue of Liberty if all four boats are used?

2. One boat carries 125 and another carries 175. Two new boats each carry the same number of people. The new boats can carry more than 175 people.

3. The number of people the new boats are able to carry.

Problem 2: The Swim Meet

1. How many yards did she swim last week?

2. Each lap is a total of 25 yards. Lily practices 4 days a week and swims the same number of laps each day.

3. The number of laps Lily swims each day.

Problem 3: At the Beach

1. What was the temperature when he left the beach?

2. The temperature rose three degrees every hour. He arrived at the beach at 10:00 a.m. and left at 2:00 p.m.

3. The temperature at the beach when Andrew arrived.

Problem 4: Football Season

1. How many points did each team score during both games?

2. The Eagles beat the Hawks 14–7 and the Falcons 21–13. The Hawks and Falcons tied.

3. The number of points scored in the tie game between the Hawks and Falcons.

Problem 5: Movie Tickets

1. How much did they spend on tickets?

2. Movie tickets cost $7.50 for adults and $3.00 for children under 12.

3. The number of children in the Meyers family and their ages.

Problem 6: Parking Meter

1. By what time does Mrs. Sanchez need to return to her car?

2. The parking meter rates are $.25 for each 15 minutes. Mrs. Sanchez put 7 quarters into the meter.

3. The time that Mrs. Sanchez parked her car.

Problem 7: Sold Out Performance

1. How much money was collected if all five performances were sold out?

2. The theater holds 125 people. There were five performances that were sold out.

3. The amount charged for each ticket.

Problem 8: The Spelling Bee

1. How many students did each school send?

2. Twenty-eight students were sent by the three schools. Edison School sent twice as many as Lincoln School.

3. The number of students sent by one of the schools.

Problem 9: Muffins

1. How much did each muffin cost?

2. Lynn bought five packages of muffins for $15.00.

3. The number of muffins in each package.

Problem 10: Postage Stamps

1. How much did Ivan pay for the stamps?

2. Ivan purchased two sheets of stamps. One sheet contained 20 stamps. Each stamp costs thirty-four cents.

3. The number of stamps on the second sheet.

Assessment Note

Students' work on any of the problems in this section can be assessed using the 3-step rubric on page ix.

Section 6 — What's the Question if You Know the Answer?

THE MATHEMATICAL SITUATIONS in Section 6 do not include questions. With the exercises in the first half of this section, students are asked to choose which one of three questions presented can be answered from the data in the situation. In the second half, students progress to writing their own questions. This section encourages reasoning and the ability to work backward from a specific answer.

It is recommended that the teaching problem that follows be used as a whole-class activity.

The procedures outlined in the teaching problem will help students understand how to

a) identify a wide range of questions that can be constructed,

b) learn how to construct a question for a specific answer.

Working in small groups or in pairs is suggested as students learn to identify the correct question or to construct questions. This will allow them to discuss their thinking with one another. Once students are comfortable with the process, they can work independently.

Whole-group discussion is especially important in this section, even after students are working independently. A question based on specific information can be framed in various ways. Discussing what makes a good question and seeing well-constructed questions modeled will help students become more proficient at writing their own good questions. Students should also talk about how they arrive at a given question. Knowing how to obtain the answer is crucial when constructing the question. It is important for the teacher as well as students to hear the thinking verbalized.

Section 6

Audio Tape Collection

Teaching Goal

After participating in this lesson students should be able to generate a variety of questions based on the given data. They should be able to construct a question for a specific answer.

Julia has 15 audio tapes. Jesse has 27 audio tapes. Maya has 41 audio tapes and Ethan has 33.

Teaching Plan

1. Write the information on the overhead projector, chalkboard, or whiteboard.

2. Have the student read the information.

3. Lead a discussion using the following questions as part of the discussion.

   There are no questions given in the information above.

   What questions can you write that could be answered with the information? List the questions students volunteer on the chalkboard, whiteboard, or overhead projector.

   What do you think the question would be if the answer is Maya? The question is *Which person has the most audio tapes?*

   What do you think the question would be if the answer were 74? *How many tapes do Maya and Ethan have together?* If the students are having trouble at this point, ask, **What numbers in the problem with what operation will give you 74?**

How did you find the answer? By adding the number of tapes that Maya has with the number that Ethan has. 41 + 33 = 74

What do you think the question is if the answer is 26? What numbers in the problem with what operation will give you 26? Students typically have more difficulty with problems when the answer is found through subtraction rather than addition. This question may take more prompting by the teacher. *How many more audio tapes does Maya have than Julia?*

How did you find the answer? By subtracting the number of audio tapes that Julia has from the number that Maya has. 41 − 15 = 26.

What do you think the question is if the answer is 116? *How many audio tapes are in the collections of all four students?*

What numbers with what operations will give you 116? How did you find the answer? By adding the number of audio tapes in each students' collection. 15 + 27 + 41 + 33 = 116

· ·

Students should be able to look at the given answer and go back to the problem and find an appropriate question. It is an excellent reasoning exercise. At first some students may have difficulty constructing questions that can be answered by a given number. If you find your students are having difficulty with this lesson, you might want to try an additional lesson or two with the whole class before asking students to continue working the next problems with a small group or in pairs.

Name
....

Problem 1 **Hospital Volunteers**

Here is a table showing the number of hours the volunteers worked at a hospital during April, May, and June.

Hours Worked

	April	May	June
Juan	20	30	20
Lara	40	26	33
Nick	25	23	20
Mieko	17	17	19

1. What's the question if the answer is 53?
Ring a, b, or c.

a. How many hours did Lara volunteer during the 3 months?

b. How many hours did Nick volunteer during the 3 months?

c. How many hours did Mieko volunteer during the 3 months?

2. What's the question if the answer is 29?
Ring a, b, or c.

a. How many more hours did Nick volunteer than Mieko?

b. How many more hours did Lara volunteer than Juan?

c. How many more hours did Lara volunteer than Nick?

Name
....

Problem 2 **The Grocery Store**

Cal bought 3 pounds of bananas at
$0.59 a pound, 3 pounds of apples at $0.99
a pound, and 2 bags of oranges at $1.39
a bag. He gave the checkout clerk a $20-bill.

1. What is the question if the
answer is $2.78?
Ring a, b, or c.

a. How much did he spend for
the bananas?

b. How much did he spend for
the oranges?

c. How much did he spend for
the apples?

2. What is question if the
answer is $7.52?
Ring a, b, or c.

a. How much did Cal pay
altogether for the groceries?

b. How much did Cal pay for
the apples and oranges?

c. How much change did Cal
get back from his $20 bill?

Problem 3 **Main Street**

Three friends live along Main Street.
Their school is also on Main Street. Hillary
lives 6 miles north of the school. Jamal lives
3.5 miles north of Hillary. Rai lives 2.5 miles
north of the school.

1. What is the question if the
answer is 9.5 miles?
Ring a, b, or c.

a. How far north of the school does
Hillary live?

b. How far north of the school does
Jamal live?

c. How far north of the school does
Rai live?

2. What is the question if the
answer is 7 miles?
Ring a, b, or c.

a. What is the distance between
Hillary's house and Jamal's house?

b. What is the distance between
Rai's house and Hillary's house?

c. What is the distance between
Rai's house and Jamal's house?

Problem 4 **Birthday Balloons**

Louise bought 12 balloons for the birthday party. Six were blue, four were yellow, and the rest were green.

1. What is the question if the answer is $\frac{1}{2}$?
Ring a, b, or c.

a. What fraction of the balloons were blue?

b. What fraction of the balloons were yellow?

c. What fraction of the balloons were green?

2. What is the question if the answer is $\frac{1}{3}$?
Ring a, b, or c.

a. What fraction of the balloons were blue?

b. What fraction of the balloons were yellow?

c. What fraction of the balloons were green?

Problem 5 **Marbles**

There are six blue marbles, four yellow marbles,
five green marbles, and three red marbles in a bag.

1. What is the question if the answer is four out of 18?

Ring a, b, or c.

a. What is the probability of picking a blue marble from the bag?

b. What is the probability of picking a yellow marble from the bag?

c. What is the probability of picking a green marble from the bag?

2. What is the question if the answer is 5 out of 18?

_____

_____

_____

3. What is the question if the answer is 0 out of 18?

_____

_____

_____

© Creative Publications 0-7622-1350-7

Name

....

Problem 6 **School Cafeteria Menu**

This is part of the menu from
the school cafeteria.

ITEM   PRICE
slice of pizza   1.25
hamburger   1.75
cold drink   0.75
salad   1.50
fresh fruit   1.00

1. What is the question if the answer is $2.25?

_____

_____

2. What is the question if the answer is $3.75?

_____

_____

3. What is the question if the answer is $6.25?

_____

_____

Name
....

Problem 7 **The Softball Game**

Here is the score from last night's softball game.

Inning	1	2	3	4	5	6	7
Lions	0	0	0	0	3	0	6
Tigers	0	0	0	2	4	0	2

1. What is the question if the answer is 9?

_____

_____

_____

2. What is the question if the answer is 1?

_____

_____

_____

3. What is the question if the answer is the seventh inning?

_____

_____

_____

 © Creative Publications 0-7622-1350-7

Problem 8 **The Bus Stop**

At the bus terminal there were 4 people on the
bus. At the first stop the bus picked up 6 people.
At the second stop 3 people got off the bus, but
8 people got on. At the third stop 5 people got
off and one got on.

1. What is the question if the answer is 10?

_____

_____

_____

2. What is the question if the answer is 15?

_____

_____

_____

3. What is the question if the answer is 11?

_____

_____

_____

Name
....

Problem 9 **The Wading Pool**

The drawing shows a wading pool surrounded by a tile walkway. Each tile is a square that measures one foot on a side.

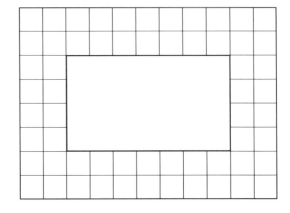

1. What is the question if the answer is 7 feet?

_____

_____

2. What is the question if the answer is 22 feet?

_____

_____

3. What is the question if the answer is 28 square feet?

_____

_____

Name
....

Problem 10 **Fast Food Pay**

Sean and Sofia work four days a week at a
fast food restaurant during summer vacation.
The following table shows the number of hours
they worked for a week and their rate of pay.

Name	Rate of Pay	Tuesday	Wednesday	Thursday	Friday
Sean	$6.25/hour	6	8	7	7
Sofia	$5.50/hour	7	7	8	8

1. What is the question if the answer is $165.00?

_____

_____

2. What is the question if the answer is 30?

_____

_____

3. What is the question if the answer is $340.00?

_____

_____

Answer Key

Problem 1: Hospital Volunteers

1. c

2. b

Problem 2: The Grocery Store

1. b

2. a

Problem 3: Main Street

1. b

2. c

Problem 4: Birthday Balloons

1. a

2. b

Problem 5: Marbles

1. b

2. What is the probability of picking a green marble from the bag?

3. What is the probability of picking a purple (or any color other than blue, yellow, green or red) marble from the bag?

Problem 6: School Cafeteria Menu

Possible questions might include

1. How much would it cost to buy a slice of pizza and a piece of fresh fruit?

2. How much would it cost to buy a slice of pizza, salad, and fresh fruit?

3. How much would it cost to buy everything on the menu?

Problem 7: The Softball Game

1. What was the Lions' final score?

2. By how many runs did the Lions beat the Tigers?
or How many more runs did the Tigers score than the Lions in the fifth inning?

3. In which inning were the most runs scored?

Problem 8: The Bus Stop

1. How many people were on the bus after the first stop?

2. How many people were on the bus after the second stop?

3. How many people were on the bus after the third stop?

Problem 9: The Wading Pool

1. What is the length of the wading pool?

2. What is the perimeter of the wading pool?

3. What is the area of the wading pool?

Problem 10: Fast Food Pay

1. How much did Sofia earn for the week?

2. How many hours did Sofia work during the week?

3. How much did Sean and Sofia earn altogether during the week?

Assessment Note

Students' work on any of the problems in this section can be assessed using the 3-step rubric on page ix.